BLAZE AND THE MONSTER MACHINES: 2018
A CENTUM BOOK 9781911460633
Published in Great Britain by Centum Books Ltd
This edition published 2017
1 3 5 7 9 10 8 6 4 2

Centum Books Ltd, 20 Devon Square, Newton Abbot, Devon, TQ12 2HR, UK
books@centumbooksltd.co.uk
CENTUM BOOKS Limited Reg. No. 07641486
A CIP catalogue record for this book is available from the British Library
Printed in China.

THIS BOOK BELONGS TO:

TRANSFORMER SPOTTER!

Can you **find** all of Blaze's transformations somewhere in this Annual?

ROLLER	FIRE ENGINE	CEMENT MIXER	WRECKING BALL	DRILL DIGGER

CONTENTS

What's under the hood?

LIGHT RIDERS

P10-11 RELAY RACE!/NEW RACER
P12-13 NUMBER SLALOM/LIGHT UP TRACKS!
P14-15 READY. SET. COLOUR!/MATCH THE MACHINE
P16-17 COMPLETE THE TRACK!/LIGHT UP ENGINES
P20-21 MAZE RACE/ START LINE MESS-UP
P22-23 MONSTER DOME DASH
P26-27 KNIGHTLY KNIGHT

WILD WHEELS

P32-33 WILD RACERS!/ JUNGLE RACERS
P34-35 WILD POSTER!/ MONSTER MEMORY!
P36-37 JUNGLE TRACKS/
ANIMAL MACHINE DESIGNER
P44-45 WILD RACING!/ CREATURE CLOSE-UPS
P40-41 THE BLAZE PACK/ GORILLA DRAW

UNDER THE HOOD

P42-43 GARAGE GRID/PIXEL TROPHY
P46-47 ENGINE SPEEDS!/ SPOT THE DIFFERENCE
P48-49 MESSAGE MIX-UP/ODD BLAZE IN!
P52-53 SPANNER FIXERS/ UNDER THE HOOD GRID
P54-55 BLUEPRINT COLOURING/
BLAZE PICTURE SEARCH
P58-59 WHERE'S THE FINISH?/
THE BLAZE SUPER-FAN QUIZ
P60-61 ANSWER TIME

PROFILES

P8 BLAZE
P18 CRUSHER
P24 DARINGTON
P30 AJ
P31 GABBY
P38 STRIPES
P44 STARLA
P50 ZEG
P56 PICKLE

WELCOME TO THE MONSTER DOME!

MONSTER MACHINE FANS, START YOUR ENGINES!

WELCOME TO THE HIGH-OCTANE WORLD OF

BLAZE AND THE MONSTER MACHINES!

INSIDE you'll discover all the awesome Monster Machine racers and their friends. There are puzzles, doodling and colouring pages, and lots of games and fun-learning activities to keep your engines running all the way to the finish line!

Look out for some cool facts along the way!

SO, ARE YOU READY TO ROLL? LET'S BLAAAZE!

BLAZE

BLAZE is the champion of the Monster Dome and the hero of Axle City. He is brave, friendly and incredibly fast!

Blaze loves learning about science and uses his know-how in all his adventures! He can also transform into lots of different machines – ready to save the day!

Blaze's best friend and driver is AJ. They are an inseparable heroic duo and work together to be the best!

BLAZING JIGSAW

Can you **match** the correct **jigsaw shapes** to the missing pieces in this Blazing picture of Blaze and his best friend AJ?

ANSWERS ON PAGE 60

COLOUR BY SPOTS

Follow the rainbow spots on the picture below and colour this high-octane picture of Blaze.

BLAZE knows a lot about **science**. Engineering, physics and **chemistry** help him, move, steer and zoom to the finish line!

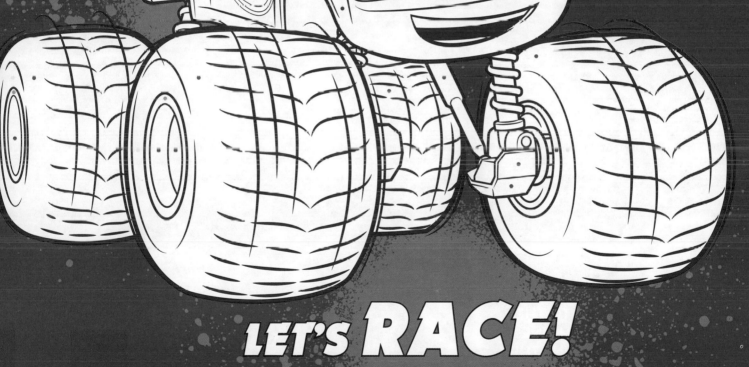

LET'S RACE!

Can you **write** Blaze's name?

Blaze

RELAY RACE!

The Monster Machines are racing in teams!
Follow the lines to find out who is in each team.

TEAM 1

TEAM 2

WHICH TEAM GETS TO THE FINISH LINE AND WINS THE TROPHY?

ANSWERS ON PAGE 50

NEW RACER

The Monster Machines have invited a new friend to race in the Light Rider Championships. **Draw what you think the new Monster Machine looks like?**

WHAT COLOUR WILL YOU PAINT YOUR MONSTER MACHINE?

Can you think of a name? Write it here.

WHICH MONSTER MACHINE IS RED? CAN YOU SPOT HIM ON THE PAGE?

NUMBER SLALOM

In a new race, the Monster Machines must steer through slalom gates on the track. **Can you guide Zeg through the correct gates?** He must steer through the gates that have odd numbers only.

STEER AND SLIDE!

FINISH

ADD up the numbers on the odd gates. what number do you get? is it odd or even?

ANSWERS ON PAGE 60

LIGHT UP TRACKS!

The Light Riders love to shine! Even their tracks light up! **Can you colour and complete these bright tyre-track patterns?**

1

2

3

4

 BLAZE

 CRUSHER

 STARLA

 DARINGTON

DO YOU KNOW WHICH tyre-track belongs to which Light Rider?

ANSWERS ON PAGE 60

READY. SET. COLOUR!

The Monster Machines are racing at the Monster Dome. **Who's going to win?**

MATCH THE MACHINE

Gabby is servicing the Monster Machines.
Can you help her match the Service Logs to the correct Monster Machines?

TRACE OVER THE STARTING LETTER OF EACH NAME TO REVEAL THE MONSTER MACHINE?

SERVICE LOG 1

BLAZE

SERVICE LOG 2

STARLA

SERVICE LOG 3

CRUSHER

SERVICE LOG 4

ZEG

SERVICE LOG 5

PICKLE

SERVICE LOG 6

DARINGTON

which LETTER does your name start with?

COMPLETE THE TRACK!

The Monster Dome is preparing the new track for the next race. **Can you help complete the track so it goes from the start line to the finish line?**

YOU NEED TO USE THE TRACK PIECES BELOW.

START

PLACE them on the grid in the correct order to complete the track. YOU can't rotate the pieces or place them on the rubble!

FINISH

A

B

C

D

E

LIGHT UP ENGINES

The Monster Machines' engine parts have been delivered to the Monster Dome. **Can you find and match the different coloured parts to the Monster Machines below?**

1

2

3

5

6

4

7

8

9

10

11

which monster machine has had THE MOST engine parts delivered?

BLAZE

STARLA

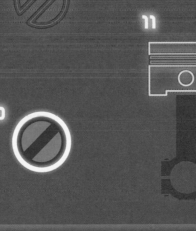
CRUSHER

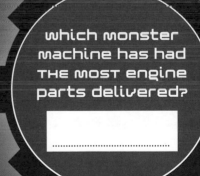
STRIPES

CRUSHER

CRUSHER is a big Monster Machine, but an even bigger baby! He doesn't like being second best to Blaze.

So, what does he do about it? He cheats! From itchy robots and a pineapple blaster to an earthquake-maker, troublemaker Crusher does whatever he can to win!

But even though Crusher is a bit of a stinker, he's still accepted as part of the Monster Dome gang.

ODD CRUSHER OUT

Can you **spot** which Crusher looks different to the others?

A   B   C

18

ANSWERS ON PAGE 60

COLOUR BY NUMBERS

Follow the numbers and colour this all-action picture of Crusher.

I'M GOING TO **WIN**... BECAUSE I'M GOING TO CHEAT!

CRUSHER puts a lot of effort into cheating. If he practised and concentrated on racing fair he might win a race!

COLOUR KEY
① ② ③ ④ ⑤

Can you **write** Crusher's name?

Crusher

MAZE RACE

Who's going to win the Maze Race? **Only one Monster Machine has a route to the finish, can you find out who wins?**

WHICH TWO MONSTER MACHINES' ROUTES COLLIDE?

AND

ANSWERS ON PAGE **60**

START LINE MESS-UP

Bump Bumperman has called the Monster Machines to the start line. But one is missing. **Can you match Bump's racing list to the racers at the start line?** Who is missing?

HOW many monster machines are in the race?

BLAZE

CRUSHER

ZEG

DARINGTON

STRIPES

STARLA

START LINE

ANSWERS ON PAGE **60**

MONSTER DOME DASH

It's the sprint race at the Monster Dome!
Who's the quickest and who will win?
Play this fun game with your friends!

YOU WILL NEED
2-4 players
a dice
coins to use as
counters

START

1

2

3
TRY DARINGTON'S TRICK JUMP SHORTCUT!
IF YOU ROLL AN EVEN NUMBER, YOU CAN TAKE THE JUMP!

14

YOU'VE GOT ENGINE TROUBLE!
MISS A TURN!
13

12

15

16

TRY CRUSHER'S SECRET TUNNEL SHORTCUT!
IF YOU ROLL AN ODD NUMBER, YOU CAN TAKE THE TUNNEL!
17

18

FINISH

29

28

YOUR WHEEL HAS COME LOOSE!
GO BACK 2 SPACES
27

HOW TO PLAY

- Each player places their coin on the Start Line square.
- The youngest player rolls first.
- Roll the dice and move the number of squares shown on the dice.
- If your coin lands on an action square, read it out loud and follow the instructions.
- There are two shortcuts, but you must land exactly on the square to have a chance of taking the shortcut!
- The first player to the Finish Line square is the winner!

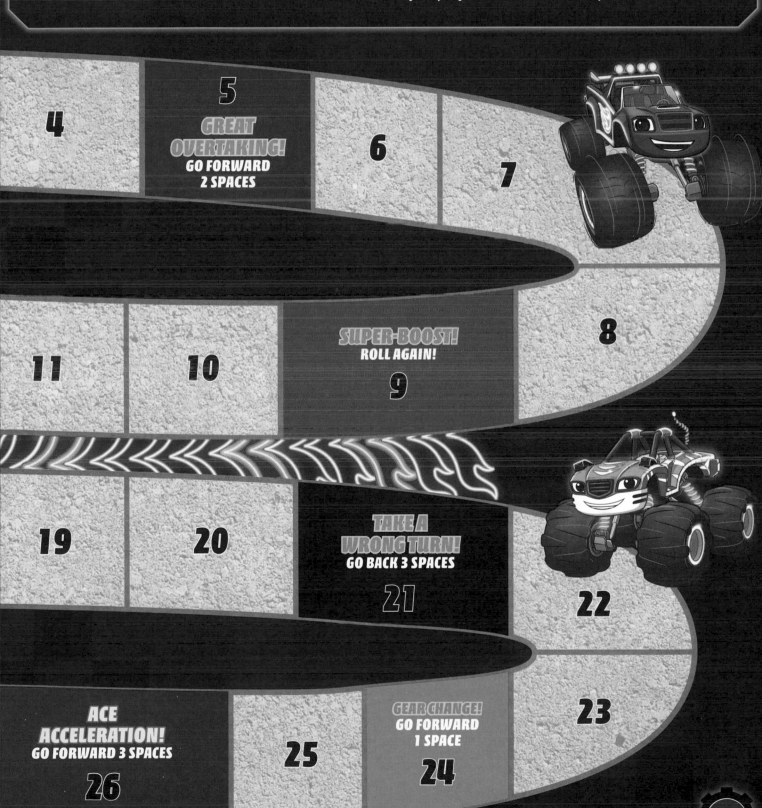

4

5
GREAT OVERTAKING!
GO FORWARD 2 SPACES

6

7

8

11

10

SUPER-BOOST!
ROLL AGAIN!
9

19

20

TAKE A WRONG TURN!
GO BACK 3 SPACES
21

22

ACE ACCELERATION!
GO FORWARD 3 SPACES
26

25

GEAR CHANGE!
GO FORWARD 1 SPACE
24

23

DARINGTON

DARINGTON is the ultimate Stunt Star who loves to dazzle the crowd with his amazing tricks and jumps.

Darington loves performing his aerial stunts, but he always comes back down to earth with a bump... or two!

ALMOST A PERFECT LANDING!

SPOT THE DARINGTON

Can you **find** 5 differences between the pictures below?

A

B

TICK OFF
a star each time you **find** one!

24

ANSWERS ON PAGE 60

DOT-TO-DARINGTON

Join the dots and find out what Darington is up to.

There are two lines, a number line and a letter line. The number line starts at '**1**' and the letter line starts at '**a**'.

Did you know that the world record for the **longest** Monster Machine jump is **72.42m**? That's as long as three tennis courts!

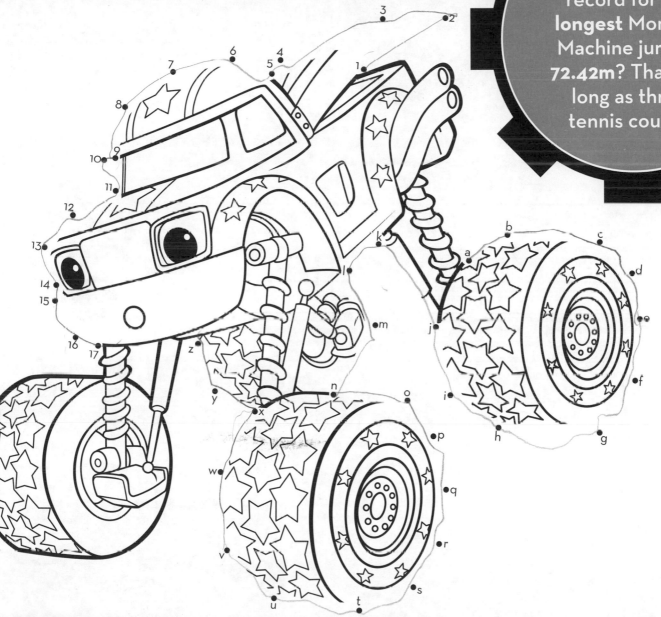

Can you **write** Darington's name?

Darington

KNIGHTLY KNIGHT

Sir Blaze and **AJ** are driving with their new royal friends, the **White**, **Purple**, **Green** and **Yellow Knights**. The Royal Knights are tired, so they take Sir Blaze to the Royal Charging Station.

"When trucks need energy, they come here to charge," explain the Royal Knights. **"Look, when the wind blows the Charging Station's turbine turns and it creates energy!"** adds Sir Blaze. **"Now, it's our turn... Let's charge!"** cry the Royal Knights, but before they can get there, a dragon swoops down, grabs the Charging Station and flies off!

"If we don't have our Royal Charging Station, no one can get charged, and no energy means the whole kingdom will fall asleep!" say the Royal Knights.

"Knights, I have a plan! We are going to follow that dragon and get the Charging Station back!" proclaims Sir Blaze.

"LET'S CHARGE!"

Sir Blaze and the Royal Knights chase the dragon to the Slime Maze.

"Slime Maze? That doesn't sound good," says Sir Blaze, as the Royal Knights charge in.

"This maze is full of Slime Vines and dead ends. How are we going to get through?" ask the Royal Knights.

"Don't worry, AJ and I can help," says Sir Blaze.

"Yes, there are lots of paths, but only one will take us past the Slime Vines and out of the maze," adds AJ.

"Lead the way, Sir Blaze!" cheer the Royal Knights. Sir Blaze and AJ dodge the dead ends and Slime Vines all the way to the exit!

"Well done! We've made it out of the.... zzzzzzzz!"

The Green and White Knights are out of energy and have fallen asleep!
The royal heroes speed off through a valley, but the dragon flies away, over a steep cliff.
"We must follow him!" says the Purple Knight.
"We can use that pulley lift!" says Sir Blaze.
"The pulley lift uses a rope and pulley wheel to lift things up to the top of the cliff!"

Sir Blaze and the Royal Knights drive onto the lift's basket and a group of friendly mountain frogs jump on the other basket at the top of the cliff. The frogs' heavy basket goes down, sending Sir Blaze and the Royal Knights up the cliff!
"We've made it to the top of the... zzzzzzz!" The Purple and Yellow Knights are now out of energy and have also fallen asleep!

"Come on AJ, we've got to get the Charging Station back and save our friends!" says Sir Blaze. Sir Blaze catches up with the high-flying dragon.
"I know what we need!" says AJ.
"A crossbow! It can shoot really far and can grab the Charging Station back from the dragon."
Sir Blaze uses a bow, string and pulley block, and transforms into a crossbow! AJ attaches a rope to an arrow, then pulls the string back... and fires! The arrow flies through the air and sticks to the Charging Station. But the dragon is strong and doesn't let go! Sir Blaze uses all his power to **PULL** and **PULL** and... **PULLS** the Charging Station from the dragon's claws!
"Yes! We've got it!" cheers AJ.

"Come on AJ, let's use blazing speed to give the kingdom some energy!" says Sir Blaze.

"Let's Blaze!" Sir Blaze zooms super-fast and charges all the trucks in the kingdom!

"You've done it, Sir Blaze! We have our Royal Charging Station back and the whole kingdom is awake!" cheer the Royal Knights.

"WATCH OUT, HERE COMES THE DRAGON AGAIN!"

The dragon flies down, but doesn't take the Charging Station, instead he falls asleep.

"The dragon isn't bad, he's just tired!" says Sir Blaze, as he uses the Charging Station to give the dragon energy. The dragon wakes up and hugs his new friends.

"Now we are friends, you can come to our castle and charge up whenever you want!" cheer the Royal Knights.

AJ

AJ is an eight-year-old Monster Machine driver who loves adventure! He is best friends with the awesome Blaze! He loves to solve problems and learn about science with his best mate.

AJ loves challenges and with the help of his helmet visor, skywriter gloves and wrist computer he is ready for anything!

H1GH TYRE!

CODE PAIRS

Can you help AJ **crack** the code and give Blaze a boost in the next race? Pair the letters and then place the letters without a pair in alphabetical order.

F D G B H F H C G E A

Can you write AJ's name?

ANSWERS ON PAGE 60

GABBY

GABBY is a nine-year-old mechanic with lots of Monster Machine know-how.

She runs the Axle City Garage and Truck Wash and is always ready to fix, upgrade or tune-up a Monster Machine in need. She's got a tool and the knowledge for every job!

LET'S GET FIXIN'!

TOOL PAIRS

Can you **match** the tools into pairs? Which tool doesn't have a pair?

Can you write **Gabby's** name?

Gabby

31

ANSWERS ON PAGE 60

WILD RACERS!

The Monster Machines have gone wheelie wild on Animal Island! **Can you match each Monster Machine to its new animal badge?**

IF YOU WERE *A WILD ANIMAL*, WHAT ANIMAL WOULD YOU BE?

CRUSHER **DARINGTON** **BLAZE** **STARLA**

A

B

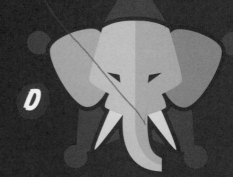

C

D

JUNGLE RACERS

The Monster Machines are racing through the Animal Island jungle. Who wins the race?

Count the number of obstacles in each path, the one with the fewest obstacles is the winner!

HOW MANY OBSTACLES ARE THERE IN TOTAL?

ANSWERS ON PAGE 60

WILD POSTER!

The Wild Wheels championships has designed a cool new poster for the Monster Machines!

ADD SOME COLOUR!

34

MONSTER MEMORY!

How good is your Monster Machine memory?
Have a look at the animal-tastic picture of the
Monster Machines for 30 seconds then cover
it up and answer the questions below.

QUESTIONS

1
WHAT ANIMAL IS STARLA?

2
WHO IS IN THE TOP RIGHT OF THE PICTURE?

3
WHAT COLOUR IS STRIPES?

4
HOW MANY MONSTER MACHINES
WERE IN THE PICTURE?

ANSWERS ON PAGE 60

WHOSE TYRE-TRACKS ARE IN THE MUDDY COURSE? CAN YOU TRACE AND WRITE THE MONSTER MACHINE'S NAME BELOW?

JUNGLE TRACKS

What a muddy racetrack! **Can you trace the route of the Wild Wheels racer?** Try to keep your line inside the guides!

Start

36

ANIMAL MACHINE DESIGNER

If you were an animal Monster Machine what animal would you choose? **Can you draw your wild ride below?**

THE FASTEST LAND ANIMAL IN THE WORLD IS THE *CHEETAH.* IT CAN RUN AT SPEEDS OF UP TO 112 KPH (70 MPH). THAT'S AS FAST AS A FAMILY CAR!

THE FASTEST ANIMAL IN THE WORLD IS THE *PEREGRINE FALCON.* IT CAN DIVE DOWN THROUGH THE SKY AT SPEEDS OF ABOUT 320 KPH (200 MPH). THAT'S AS FAST AS A *FORMULA-1 RACING CAR!*

STRIPES

STRIPES IS A HOT-HEADED TIGER TRUCK who is always ready for action. He loves to growl, leap and pounce! He's a brilliant climber, but when he falls he always lands on his tyres. He also has a super-smell sense and can sniff out victory!

STRIPES PUZZLE

Can you **complete** the puzzle of Stripes? Which piece doesn't belong to the picture?

CAMOUFLAGE COLOURING

Can you follow the numbers and colour in this hidden picture of Stripes?

DID YOU KNOW THAT NO TWO TIGERS HAVE THE SAME STRIPY FUR PATTERN?

CAN YOU WRITE STRIPES'S NAME?

Stripes

THE BLAZE PACK

Blaze can transform into lots of awesome animals!

Can you match the pictures of Blaze to the wild shadows?

DID YOU KNOW THAT *THE TIGER SHARK* IS KNOWN AS THE GARBAGE CAN OF THE SEA? IT WILL EAT ANYTHING IT THINKS IS FOOD... EVEN OLD TYRES AND LICENCE PLATES!

WHICH SHADOW DOESN'T HAVE A MATCHING BLAZE PICTURE?

A

B

C

D

1

2

3

4

5

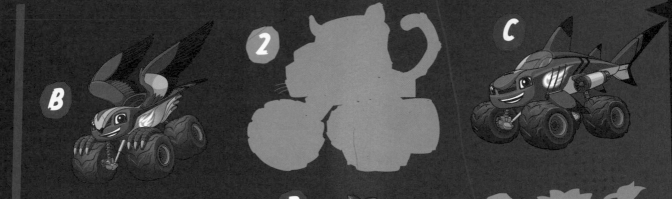

GORILLA DRAW

Blaze has changed into a gorilla!

Can you copy draw the picture of Blaze?

Use the grid and guidelines to help you.

GARAGE GRID

Gabby and AJ are recycling the spare parts at the Axle City Garage. **Can you find the matching pairs in the grid?**

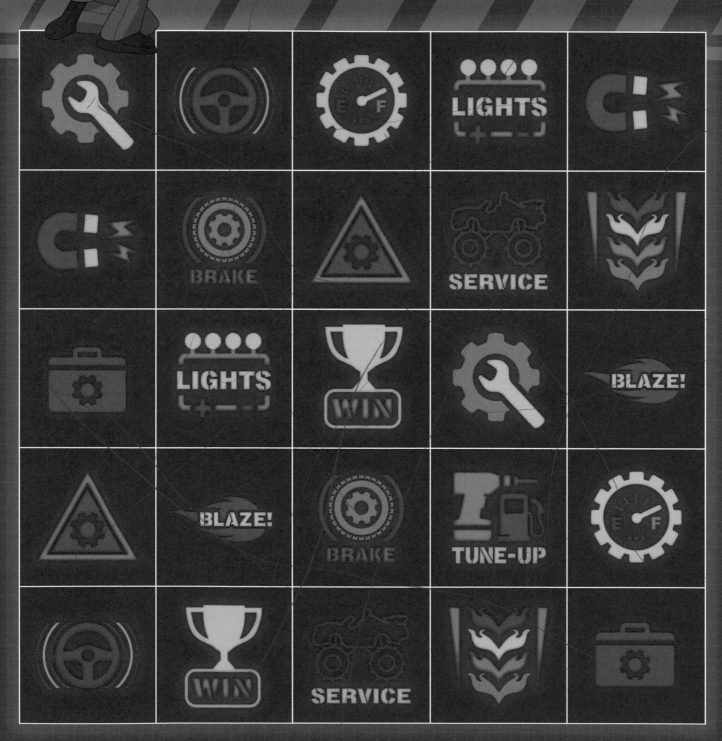

WHICH COOL ITEM DOESN'T HAVE A PAIR?

ANSWERS ON PAGE 61

PIXEL TROPHY

The new Power Pixel Championships needs a trophy!
Use the square paper below to draw a cool design.

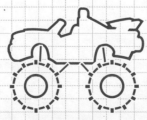

COLOUR THE SQUARES TO CREATE YOUR PIXEL TROPHY!

DESIGNED TO WIN!

STARLA

STARLA is a hootin', tootin' cowgirl Monster Machine.

She is the only girl racer on the team, but can speed-it with the best of them! She loves singing, especially country ballads, and has a cowgirl hat and handy lasso.

A **TEAM** is a group that works together.

STARLA DIFFERENCE

Can you **spot** the 5 differences between these pictures?

ANSWERS ON PAGE 61

COLOUR BY LETTERS

Follow the colour-letter key below and **colour in** this action pose of the speedy Starla!

COLOUR KEY

k	PINK
p	**PURPLE**
b	BLUE
g	GREY
y	YELLOW

Can you **write** Starla's name?

Starla

ENGINE SPEEDS!

SPEED **SPEED**

How fast do you think the Monster Machines can go?
**Count the symbols in each box then write the number
in each dial. When you have all the dial numbers,
then you have their top speeds!**

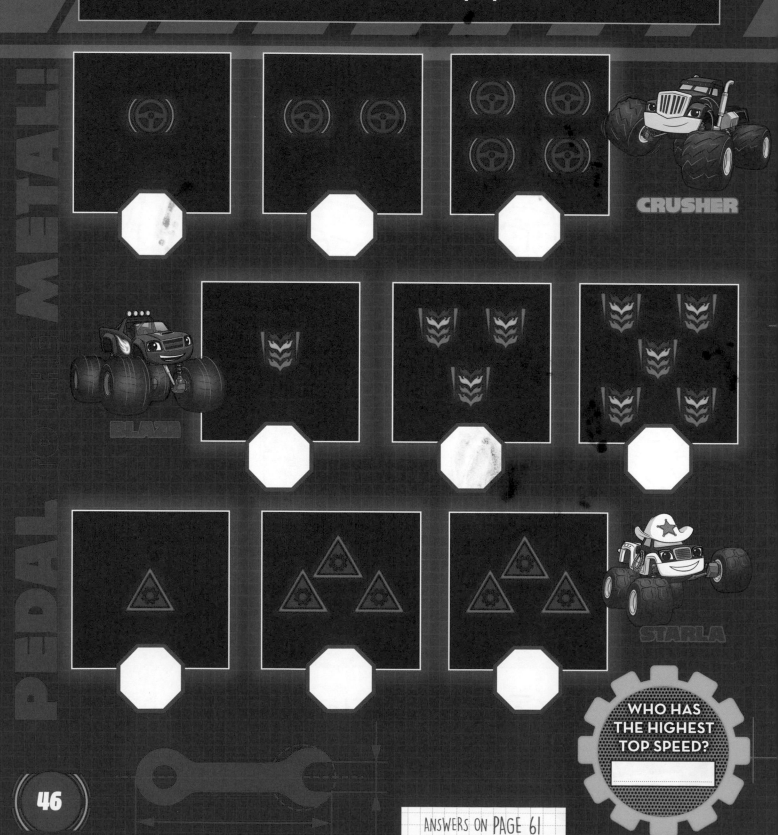

CRUSHER

BLAZE

STARLA

PEDAL TO THE METAL!

WHO HAS
THE HIGHEST
TOP SPEED?

ANSWERS ON PAGE 61

SPOT THE DIFFERENCE

What a cool poster of Blaze! **Can you spot 6 differences between the road-ready posters?**

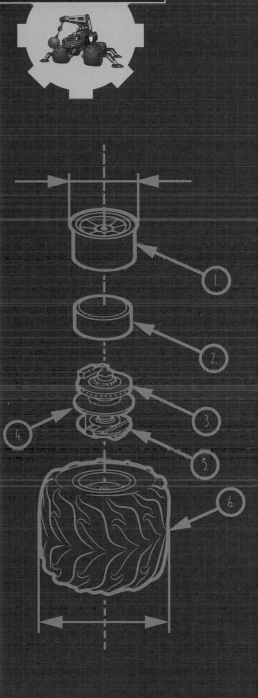

CAN YOU TRACE AND WRITE READY TO ROLL?

Ready to roll

MESSAGE MIX-UP

Gabby is called to the Monster Dome to fix some of the Monster Machines. But on the message, all the names are scrambled up! **Can you work out which Monster Machines need Gabby's help?**

A RALAST

B NOTARNIGD

C ZALBE

D LICKEP

E RUSCRHE

CAN YOU TRACE AND WRITE GABBY'S NAME ON HER TOOLBOX?

Gabby

ANSWERS ON PAGE 61

ODD BLAZE IN!

Pickle is trying to find the real Blaze among lots of fans dressed up in Blaze costumes! **Can you help him find the real racer?** Blaze is the one that looks different to all the others!

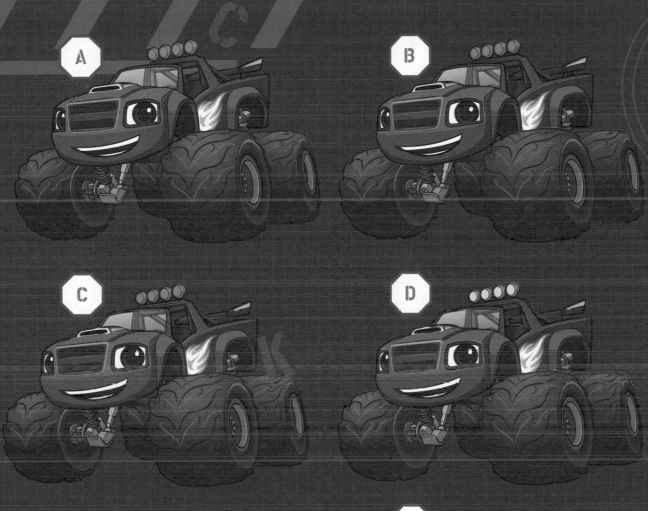

A   B   C   D   E

CAN YOU FIND ALL THE RED LETTERS ON THE PAGE THAT SPELL PICKLE?

ZEG

Zeg is a mighty dinosaur truck and a loveable lugnut!

His curved exhaust pipes make him look like his favourite dino, the Triceratops. Nothing makes Zeg happier than a smash-and-bash race around the Monster Dome!

ZEG PAIRS

Can you match the Zeg pairs? Which Zeg doesn't have a pair?

A   **B**   **C**   **D**   **E**

50

ANSWERS ON PAGE 61

DOTTY DINO RACER!

Join the dots to draw this dinosaur-tastic picture of Zeg.
There are two lines, a number line and a letter line. The number line starts at '1' and the letter line starts at 'a'.

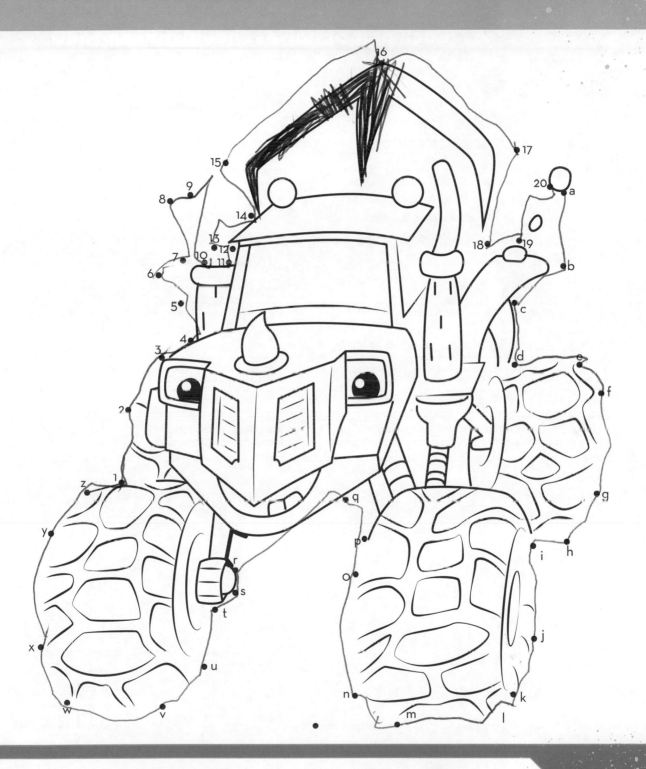

Can you **write** Zeg's name?

SPANNER FIXERS

AJ and Gabby are fixing the spanners in the Axle City Garage. **Can you match the halves? Each pair of halves should add up to 10.**

9

5

1

5

2

7

4

8

3

6

CAN YOU FIX THE FUEL NUMBER LINE BELOW? FILL IN THE MISSING NUMBERS.

LIGHTS

| 1 | | | 4 | 5 | | 7 | 8 | | 10 |

ANSWERS ON PAGE 61

UNDER THE HOOD GRID

Can you give Blaze a tune-up? **Complete the service icons in the engine grid below.** There can only be one icon type in each row and column.

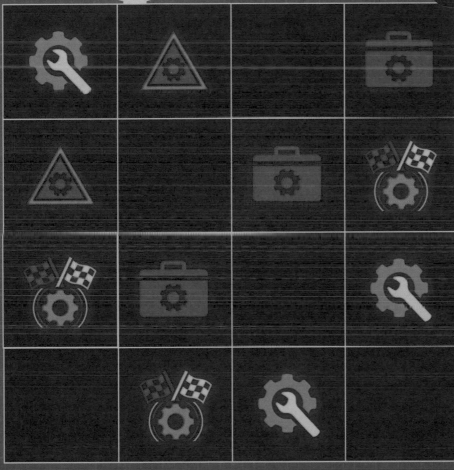

A MONSTER MACHINE'S ENGINE IS KNOWN AS A COMBUSTION ENGINE. INSIDE THE ENGINE, SMALL EXPLOSIONS CREATE MECHANICAL MOVEMENT THAT CREATES THE POWER TO MOVE THE WHEELS!

1

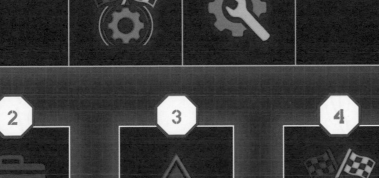

2   **3**   **4**   **5**

BLUEPRINT COLOURING

AJ has found the blueprints for **BLAZE.**
Get your favourite pens ready and colour them in!

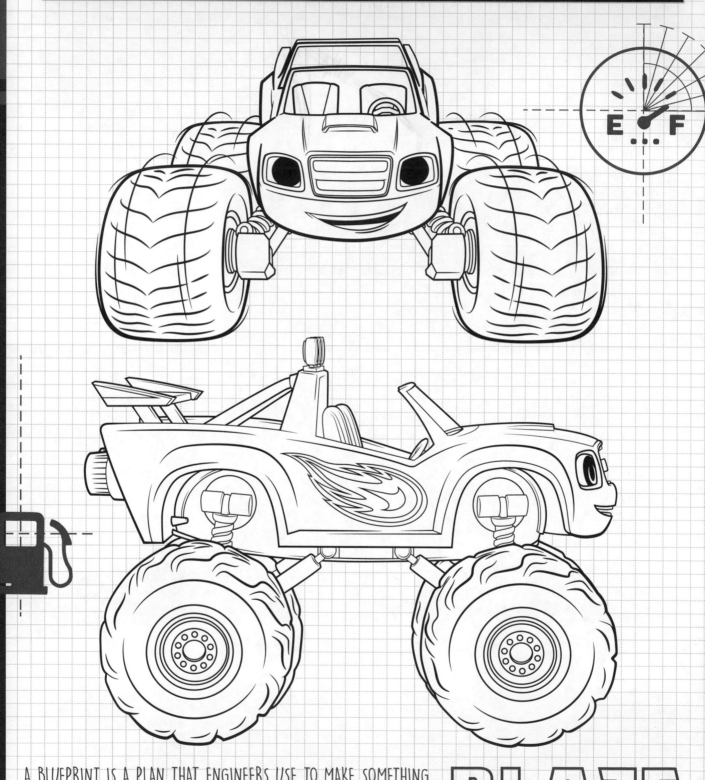

A BLUEPRINT IS A PLAN THAT ENGINEERS USE TO MAKE SOMETHING.
MONSTER MACHINES, BUILDINGS, BRIDGES, EVEN COMPUTERS HAVE
BLUEPRINT PLANS MADE BEFORE THEY ARE BUILT.

BLAZE

BLAZE PICTURE SEARCH

It's a busy day at the Monster Dome. **Can you help AJ find the garage patterns in the grid below.**

 CAN YOU SPOT THE TROPHY IN THE GRID?

PICKLE

PICKLE is Crusher's loyal sidekick. He is a loveable Mini-Monster Machine who sees the best in Crusher and tries to help him whenever he can. Don't tell Crusher... but Pickle is also a huge Blaze fan!

PICKLE PRACTICE

FINISH

Can you use your finger to **guide** Pickle across the windy track? Try to keep inside the guidelines.

PICKLE POSTER

WHAT A PICKLE

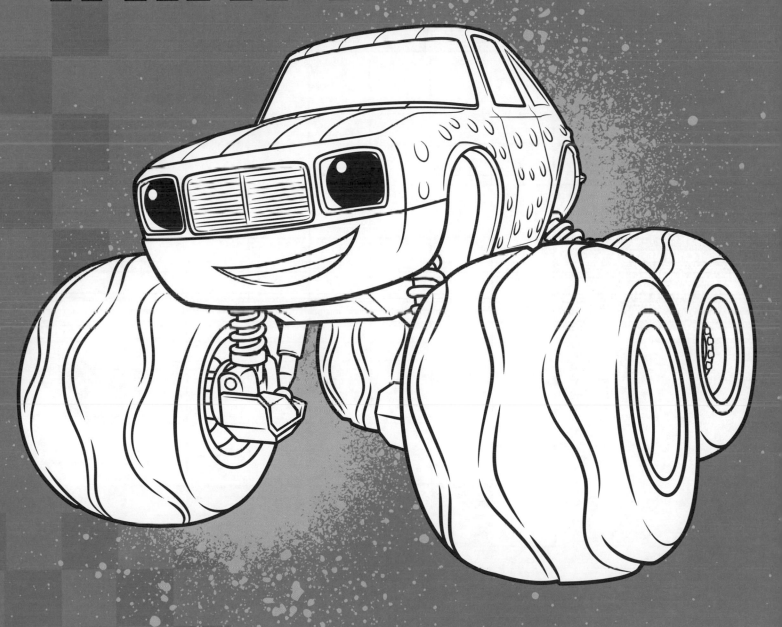

Can you **write** Pickle's name?

Pickle

WHERE'S THE FINISH?

Oh, no! Blaze has spun off the track and has lost his way. He can see lots of finish lines! **Can you guide him across the track and get him to the correct finish line?**

READ THE DIRECTIONS TO FIND THE CORRECT FINISH LINE.

RIGHT	4
DOWN	4
LEFT	2
DOWN	1
RIGHT	4
UP	2
RIGHT	1

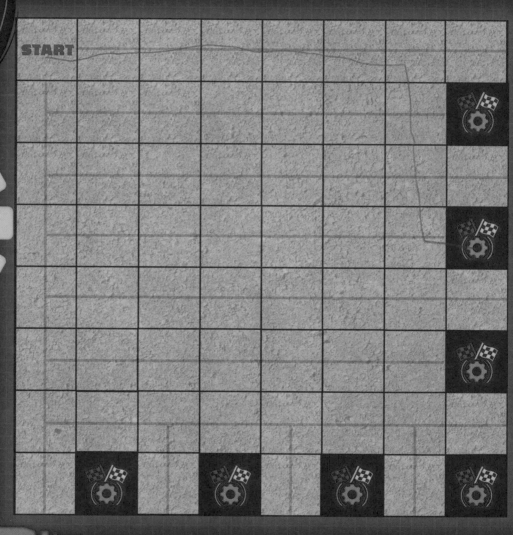

START

ROAD
READY!

ANSWERS ON PAGE 61

THE BLAZE SUPER-FAN QUIZ

Are you a Blaze super-fan? **Put yourself to the test and answer the true-or-false statements below!**

1	**PICKLE** is Darington's sidekick	TRUE OR FALSE
2	**ZEG** is a dinosaur Monster Machine	TRUE OR FALSE
3	**BLAZE** can transform into lots of cool vehicles	TRUE OR FALSE
4	**AJ** is Starla's driver	TRUE OR FALSE
5	**GABBY** works at the Axle City Garage	TRUE OR FALSE
6	**DARINGTON** is very safe and doesn't like big jumps	TRUE OR FALSE
7	**STRIPES** is a lion Monster Machine	TRUE OR FALSE
8	The Monster Machines **RACE** at the Monster Dome	TRUE OR FALSE
9	**CRUSHER** never cheats!	TRUE OR FALSE

1–3 CORRECT	4–6 CORRECT	7+ CORRECT
Good try, but it looks like you might **NEED A TUNE-UP!**	You know your stuff, soon you'll be **READY TO RACE!**	You truly are a **BLAZING SUPER-FAN! WELL DONE!**

ANSWERS ON PAGE 61

ANSWER TIME!

PAGE 8

PAGE 10

Team 1: Darington, Starla, Blaze.
Team 2: Stripes, Crusher, Zeg.
Team 1 gets to the finish line and wins the trophy.

PAGE 12

Route C: 1 + 3 + 5 = **9**.
9 is an **odd** number.

PAGE 13

1. Starla, **2.** Darington, **3.** Crusher, **4.** Blaze.

PAGE 16

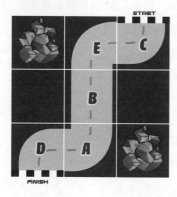

PAGE 17

Blaze's parts are **1, 2, 6** and **8**,
Starla's parts are **4** and **11**,
Crusher's parts are **3, 7** and **10**,
Stripes' parts are **5** and **9**.
Blaze has the most engine parts delivered.

PAGE 18

Crusher **B** is the odd one out.

PAGE 20

Zeg is the winner. **Crusher** and
Pickle's routes collide.

PAGE 21

Darington is missing from the starting line.

PAGE 24

PAGE 30

A, B, C, D, E.

PAGE 31

PAGE 32

A: Blaze, **B:** Crusher, **C:** Darington, **D:** Starla.

PAGE 33

The winner is **Blaze**.
There are **12** obstacles in total.

PAGE 35

Starla is an **Elephant**.
Stripes is **orange and purple**.
Stripes is in the top right of the picture.
There were **4** Monster Machines in the picture.

PAGE 38

Piece number 1 does not
belong in the puzzle.

PAGE 40

A: 5, **B:** 1, **C:** 4, **D:** 3.
Shadow 2 does not have
a matching Blaze picture.

ANSWER TIME!

PAGE 42
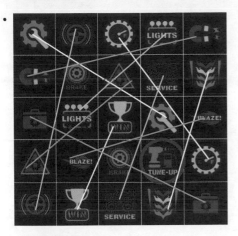

PAGE 44

PAGE 46
Crusher: **124**, Blaze: **135**, Starla: **133**.
Blaze has the highest top speed.

PAGE 47

PAGE 48
A: Starla, **B:** Darington, **C:** Blaze,
D: Pickle, **E:** Crusher.

PAGE 49
D is the real Blaze.

PAGE 50
A+C, B+D.
E doesn't have a pair.

PAGE 52

1	2	3	4	5	6	7	8	9	10

PAGE 53

PAGE 55
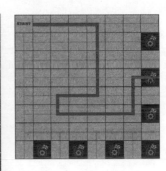

PAGE 58
START

PAGE 59
1: FALSE, **2:** TRUE,
3: TRUE, **4:** FALSE,
5: TRUE, **6:** FALSE,
7: FALSE, **8:** TRUE,
9: FALSE.

DID YOU
FIND ALL THE
**HIDDEN
TRANSFORMATIONS**
IN THE BOOK?
GO BACK AND SEE
IF YOU CAN FIND
THEM ALL!

Roller – Page 17,
Fire Engine – Page 25,
Cement Mixer – Page 41,
Wrecking Ball – Page 47,
Drill Digger – Page 53.

61